2 This passage is for SATB choir, written in short score. Rewrite it in open score.

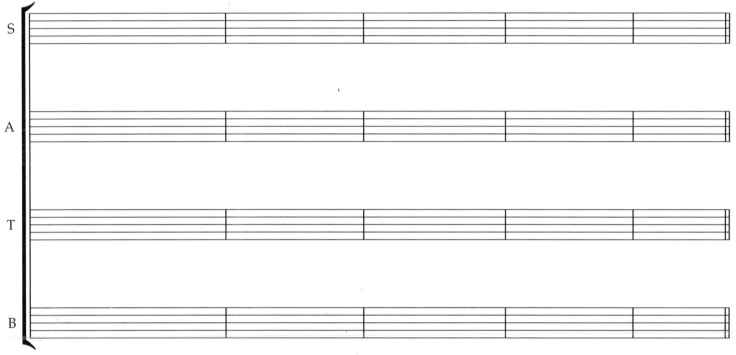

3 Look at this extract, which is adapted from a song for bass voice and piano by Cornelius, and then answer the questions that follow.

(a) (i) Give the meaning of:

   Ruhig .... (2)

   legato (piano, bar 5) .... (2)

   (ii) Complete the following statement:

   All the notes in the piano part of bars 6–7 can be found in the scale of ……… major. (2)

   (iii) Rewrite the first two notes in the voice part of bar 2 (marked ) so that they sound at the same pitch, but using the tenor C clef. Remember to put in the clef and the key signature.

(4)

(b) (i) Add the correct rest(s) at the place marked * to complete bar 3 of the voice part. (2)

(ii) Describe the time signature as: simple or compound .... (1)

duple, triple or quadruple .... (1)

(iii) Give the technical names (e.g. tonic, dominant) of the two notes in the voice part marked **A** and **B**. The key is B minor.

A (bar 1) .... **B** (bar 2) .... (4)

(iv) Write as a breve (double whole-note) an enharmonic equivalent of the last voice note of the extract.

(2)

(c) (i) Answer TRUE or FALSE to each of the following statements:

The largest melodic interval between two notes next to each other in the voice part of this extract is a diminished 4th. .... (2)

The chord marked **X** in the piano part of bar 1 is a subdominant chord in second inversion (IVc) in the key of B minor. .... (2)

(ii) Give the name of the voice part which lies between tenor and bass in vocal range.

.... (2)

(iii) Name a standard orchestral instrument that could play the voice part of the extract so that it sounds at the same pitch, and state the family to which it belongs.

Instrument .... Family .... (4)

4 (a) Using semibreves (whole notes), write one octave **ascending** of the **melodic** minor scale that begins on the given note. Do *not* use a key signature but put in all necessary sharp or flat signs. [10]

(b) Write the key signature of four flats and then one octave **descending** of the major scale with that key signature. Use semibreves (whole notes) and begin on the tonic.

5 The following melody is written for clarinet in B♭. Transpose it *down* a major 2nd, as it will sound at concert pitch. Remember to put in the new key signature and add any necessary accidentals. [10]

Bading, Caprice, Op. 14 (adapted)

(a) Compose a complete melody for unaccompanied violin or trumpet, using the given opening. **Put in the tempo, dynamics and other performance directions as appropriate**. The complete melody should be eight bars long.

Instrument for which the melody is written: ....

OR

(b) Compose a complete melody to the following words for a solo voice. Write each syllable under the note or notes to which it is to be sung. Also **put in the tempo, dynamics and other performance directions as appropriate**.

> I have made for you a song,
> And it may be right or wrong.
>
> *Rudyard Kipling*

7 Suggest suitable progressions for two cadences in the following melody by indicating ONLY ONE chord (I, II, IV or V) at each of the places marked A–E. You do not have to indicate the position of the chords, or to state which note is in the bass.

Show the chords:

EITHER   (a)   by writing I, II etc. or any other recognized symbols on the dotted lines below;

OR   (b)   by writing notes on the staves.

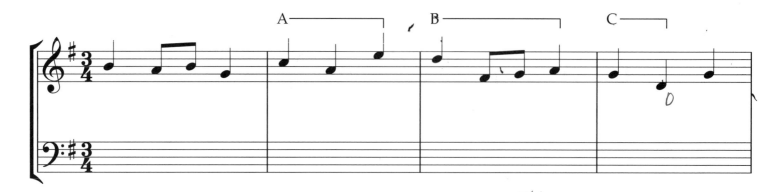

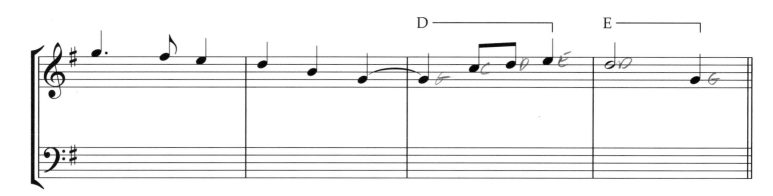

FIRST CADENCE:

Chord A   ....

Chord B   ....

Chord C   ....

SECOND CADENCE:

Chord D   ....

Chord E   ....

BLANK PAGE

Theory Paper   Grade 5   2016   B

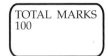 It is **illegal** to make unauthorized copies of this copyright music.

Duration 2 hours

This paper contains SEVEN questions, ALL of which should be answered.
Write your answers on this paper – no others will be accepted.
Answers must be written clearly and neatly – otherwise marks may be lost.

TOTAL MARKS
100

15

1 (a) Rewrite the following extract with the notes correctly grouped (beamed).

Bruhns, *Nun komm, der Heiden Heiland* (adapted)

(6)

(b) Look at the following extract and then answer the questions below.

Haydn, Keyboard Sonata, Hob. XVI/38 (adapted)

(i) Describe the chords marked $\boxed{A}$ and $\boxed{B}$ as I, II, IV or V. Also indicate whether the lowest note of the chord is the root (a), 3rd (b) or 5th (c). The key is C minor.

Chord **A** (bar 2)   ....   (2)

Chord **B** (bar 3)   ....   (2)

(ii) Name the ornament in the right-hand part of bar 3.   ....   (2)

(iii) Rewrite the first right-hand note of the extract so that it sounds at the same pitch, but using the alto C clef. Remember to put in the clef and the key signature.

(3)

2 Describe fully each of the numbered and bracketed melodic intervals (e.g. major 2nd). [10]

Rønnes, Bassoon Sonata No. 5

© Copyright Robert Rønnes
Reproduced by permission.
Published by Robert Rønnes Publications, Stavanger, Norway, www.robertronnes.com

Intervals:

1 ....

2 ....

3 ....

4 ....

5 ....

3 The following melody is written for horn in F. Transpose it *down* a perfect 5th, as it will sound at concert pitch. Do *not* use a key signature but remember to put in all necessary sharp, flat or natural signs. [10]

Belloli, No. 3 from 8 Etudes for horn

4 Look at this extract, which is adapted from a piano piece by Smetana, and then answer the questions that follow.

Allegro comodo, sempre marcato

(a) (i) **Mark clearly on the music**, using the appropriate capital letter for identification, one example of each of the following. Also give the bar number(s) of each of your answers, as shown in the answer to **A**. [10]

    A a tie in the left-hand part. Bars ......2–3......

    B in the left-hand part, a sign that means to spread the
       notes of the chord quickly, starting from the bottom note. Bar .... (2)

    C an instruction to play the notes sweetly. Bar .... (2)

    D in bars 3–6 of the right-hand part, a leading note
       in the key of E minor (circle the note concerned). Bar .... (2)

(ii) Rewrite the first right-hand chord of bar 7 (marked ↓) so that it sounds at the same pitch, but using the tenor C clef. Remember to put in the clef and the key signature.

(4)

12

(b) (i) Give the meaning of:
10

comodo .... (2)

sempre .... (2)

marcato .... (2)

sf (e.g. left hand, bar 5) .... (2)

(ii) The extract begins in the key of E minor. In which key does it end? .... (2)

(c) (i) Answer TRUE or FALSE to each of the following statements:
10

Vite has a similar meaning to **Allegro**. .... (2)

All the notes in bar 7 can be found in the scale of E *harmonic* minor. .... (2)

(ii) Name a standard orchestral instrument that could play the left-hand part of bars 3–4 so that it sounds at the same pitch, and state the family of instruments to which it belongs.

Instrument .... Family .... (4)

(iii) Underline *one* instrument from the list below that is a member of the orchestral percussion family.

oboe   viola   trumpet   marimba   (2)

5 (a) Put accidentals in front of the notes that need them to form the scale of G♯ **harmonic** minor. Do *not* use a key signature.
10

(b) Write the key signature of E♭ major and then one octave **ascending** of that scale. Use semibreves (whole notes) and begin on the tonic.

(a) Compose a complete melody for unaccompanied oboe or flute, using the given opening. **Put in the tempo, dynamics and other performance directions as appropriate**. The complete melody should be eight bars long.

Instrument for which the melody is written: ....

OR

(b) Compose a complete melody to the following words for a solo voice. Write each syllable under the note or notes to which it is to be sung. Also **put in the tempo, dynamics and other performance directions as appropriate**.

And on the bay the moonlight lay,
And the shadow of the moon.

Samuel Taylor Coleridge

7 Suggest suitable progressions for two cadences in the following melody by indicating ONLY ONE chord (I, II, IV or V) at each of the places marked A–E. You do not have to indicate the position of the chords, or to state which note is in the bass.

Show the chords:

EITHER   (a)   by writing I, II etc. or any other recognized symbols on the dotted lines below;

OR   (b)   by writing notes on the staves.

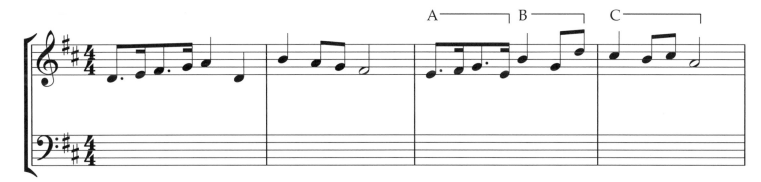

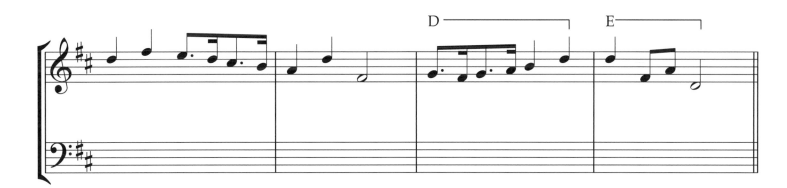

FIRST CADENCE: SECOND CADENCE:

Chord A ....

                                                  Chord D ....

Chord B ....

                                                  Chord E ....

Chord C ....

Theory Paper   Grade 5   2016   C

It is **illegal** to make unauthorized copies of this copyright music.

Duration 2 hours

This paper contains SEVEN questions, ALL of which should be answered.
Write your answers on this paper – no others will be accepted.
Answers must be written clearly and neatly – otherwise marks may be lost.

TOTAL MARKS
100

1 (a) The following extract begins on the first beat of the bar and contains some changes
of time signature. Put in the correct time signatures at the three places marked ∗.

Bartók, Violin Sonata No. 2

(6)

© Copyright 1923 by Universal Edition A. G., Wien
Copyright renewed 1950 by Boosey & Hawkes, Inc.
All rights in the USA owned and controlled by Boosey & Hawkes, Inc., New York.
Reproduced by permission. All rights reserved.

(b) Look at the following extract and then answer the questions below.

Handel, *Brockes Passion*, HWV 48

etc.

(i) Describe the chords marked [A] and [B] as I, II, IV or V. Also indicate whether the lowest
note of the chord is the root (a), 3rd (b) or 5th (c). The key is A major.

Chord **A** (bar 1)   ……………………………………   (2)

Chord **B** (bar 1)   ……………………………………   (2)

(ii) Below the staves write Ic–V ($^6_4$ $^5_3$) under the *two successive* chords where this
progression occurs. Remember that the key is A major.   (2)

(iii) Rewrite the first two left-hand notes of the extract so that they sound at the
same pitch, but using the alto C clef. Remember to put in the key signature.

(3)

2 Describe fully each of the numbered and bracketed melodic intervals (e.g. major 3rd). `10`

Berg, Violin Concerto

© Copyright 1935 by Universal Edition A. G., Wien
All rights reserved. Reproduced by permission.

Intervals:

1 ....

2 ....

3 ....

4 ....

5 ....

3 These are the actual sounds made by a clarinet in A. Rewrite the passage as it would appear for the player to read, that is, transpose it *up* a minor 3rd. Do *not* use a key signature but remember to put in all necessary sharp, flat or natural signs. `10`

Mozart, Clarinet Concerto K. 622

4 Look at this extract, which is adapted for trumpet from a piece for cello and piano by Auguste van Biene, and then answer the questions that follow.

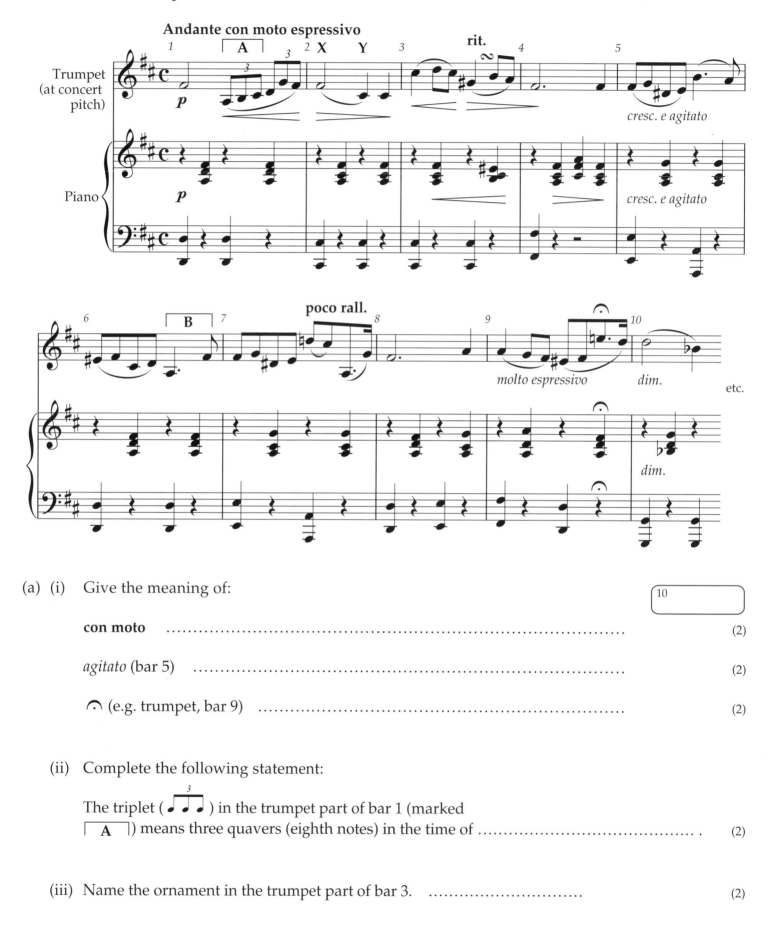

(a) (i) Give the meaning of:

10

con moto .... (2)

agitato (bar 5) .... (2)

⌢ (e.g. trumpet, bar 9) .... (2)

(ii) Complete the following statement:

The triplet (🎵) in the trumpet part of bar 1 (marked
[A]) means three quavers (eighth notes) in the time of .... (2)

(iii) Name the ornament in the trumpet part of bar 3. .... (2)

(b) (i) Rewrite the last two trumpet notes of bar 6 (marked ⌐ B ⌐) so that they sound [10] at the same pitch, but using the tenor C clef. Remember to put in the clef and the key signature.

(4)

(ii) Give the technical names (e.g. tonic, dominant) of the two notes in the trumpet part of bar 2 marked **X** and **Y**. The key is D major.

X ....   (2)

Y ....   (2)

(iii) Complete the following statement:

All the notes in the piano part of bar 3 can be found in the scale of .... minor.   (2)

(c) (i) Write as a breve (double whole-note) an enharmonic equivalent of the last [10] trumpet note of the extract.

(2)

(ii) Complete the following statements:

The trumpet is a member of the .... family of standard orchestral instruments.   (2)

The lowest-sounding member of this family is the ....   (2)

(iii) Name two standard orchestral percussion instruments, one that produces sounds of definite pitch and one that produces sounds of indefinite pitch.

Definite pitch   ....   (2)

Indefinite pitch   ....   (2)

5 (a) Using semibreves (whole notes), write one octave **ascending** of the **chromatic** [10] scale that begins on the given note. Remember to put in all necessary sharp, flat or natural signs.

(b) Using semibreves (whole notes), write one octave **descending** of the **harmonic** minor scale that has the given key signature. Begin on the tonic and remember to include any necessary additional sharp, flat or natural signs.

(a) Compose a complete melody for unaccompanied trombone or cello, using the given opening. **Put in the tempo, dynamics and other performance directions as appropriate**. The complete melody should be eight bars long.

Instrument for which the melody is written: ....

OR

(b) Compose a complete melody to the following words for a solo voice. Write each syllable under the note or notes to which it is to be sung. Also **put in the tempo, dynamics and other performance directions as appropriate**.

Lark song and sea sounds in the air
And splendour, splendour everywhere.

Sir John Betjeman

Seaside Golf, from Collected Poems, by John Betjeman
© 1955, 1958, 1962, 1964, 1968, 1970, 1979, 1981, 1982, 2001.
Reproduced by permission of John Murray, an imprint of Hodder and Stoughton Ltd.

7 Suggest suitable progressions for two cadences in the following melody by indicating ONLY ONE chord (I, II, IV or V) at each of the places marked A–E. You do not have to indicate the position of the chords, or to state which note is in the bass.

10

Show the chords:

EITHER   (a)   by writing I, II etc. or any other recognized symbols on the dotted lines below;

OR   (b)   by writing notes on the staves.

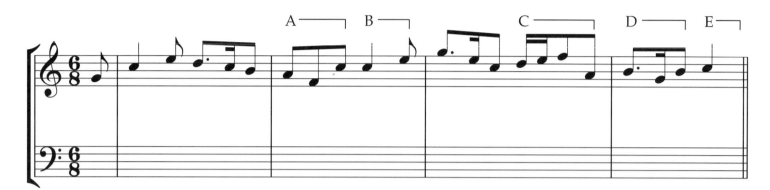

FIRST CADENCE:

Chord A ....

Chord B ....

SECOND CADENCE:

Chord C ....

Chord D ....

Chord E ....

BLANK PAGE

Theory Paper   Grade 5   2016   S

It is **illegal** to make unauthorized copies of this copyright music.

Duration 2 hours

TOTAL MARKS
100

This paper contains SEVEN questions, ALL of which should be answered.
Write your answers on this paper – no others will be accepted.
Answers must be written clearly and neatly – otherwise marks may be lost.

1 (a) Look at the following extract and then answer the questions below.

15

Handel, *Messiah* (adapted)

etc.

(i)   Describe the chords marked ⏢A⏢, ⏢B⏢ and ⏢C⏢ as I, II, IV or V. Also indicate whether
the lowest note of the chord is the root (a), 3rd (b) or 5th (c). The key is G minor.

Chord **A**   ....   (2)

Chord **B**   ....   (2)

Chord **C**   ....   (2)

(ii) Which other key has the
same key signature as G minor?   Key: ....   (2)

(b) Look at the following extract and then answer the questions below.

Mozart, Fantasia, K. 475

etc.

(i)   The extract begins on the first beat of the bar. Put in the missing bar-lines.   (3)

(ii) Write as a breve (double whole-note) an enharmonic equivalent of the note marked ↓.

(2)

(iii) Give the time name (e.g. crotchet or
quarter note) of the *shortest rest* in the extract.   ....   (2)

2 This passage is for SATB choir, written in open score. Rewrite it in short score.

Arcadelt, *At trepida et coeptis immanibus effera Dido*

3 Look at this extract, which is adapted from Reger's *Romanze* for violin and piano, and then answer the questions that follow.

(a) (i) Give the meaning of:

10

{ (right-hand piano, bar 8) .... (2)

agitato (bar 9) .... (2)

stringendo (bar 9) .... (2)

(ii) Rewrite the last right-hand piano chord of the extract (marked ↓) so that it sounds at the same pitch, but using the tenor C clef. Remember to put in the clef and the key signature.

(4)

(b) (i) Describe fully each of the numbered and bracketed harmonic intervals *in the* [10]
piano part (e.g. major 2nd).

1 (bar 1, right hand)   ……………………………………………………… (2)

2 (bar 3, left hand)   ……………………………………………………… (2)

3 (bar 6, right hand)   ……………………………………………………… (2)

(ii) Rewrite the violin part of bar 4 in simple time but without changing the rhythmic effect.
Remember to include the new time signature.

(4)

(c) (i) Complete the following statement: [10]

All the notes in bars 3–4 of the
piano part can be found in the scale of ……… major. (2)

(ii) Give the technical names (e.g. tonic, dominant) of the two notes in the violin part marked
A and **B**. The key is G major.

A (bar 1)   …………………………… (2)

B (bar 2)   …………………………… (2)

(iii) The violin is a member of the string family of orchestral instruments. Name a *different*
family of standard orchestral instruments and state its highest-sounding member.

Family   ……………………………   Instrument   ………………………………… (4)

4 (a) Using semibreves (whole notes), write one octave **descending** of the **harmonic** [10] minor scale that begins on the given note. Do *not* use a key signature but put in all necessary sharp or flat signs.

(b) Write the key signature of five sharps and then one octave **ascending** of the major scale with that key signature. Use semibreves (whole notes) and begin on the tonic.

5 These are the actual sounds made by a cor anglais. Rewrite the passage as it would [10] appear for the player to read, that is, transpose it *up* a perfect 5th. Do *not* use a key signature but remember to put in all necessary sharp, flat or natural signs.

Draeseke, *Kleine Suite*, Op. 87

etc.

(a) Compose a complete melody for unaccompanied bassoon or cello, using the given opening. **Put in the tempo, dynamics and other performance directions as appropriate**. The complete melody should be eight bars long.

Instrument for which the melody is written: …………………………

OR

(b) Compose a complete melody to the following words for a solo voice. Write each syllable under the note or notes to which it is to be sung. Also **put in the tempo, dynamics and other performance directions as appropriate**.

> And hand in hand, on the edge of the sand,
> They danced by the light of the moon.   *Edward Lear*

7 Suggest suitable progressions for two cadences in the following melody by indicating ONLY ONE chord (I, II, IV or V) at each of the places marked A–E. You do not have to indicate the position of the chords, or to state which note is in the bass.

Show the chords:

EITHER   (a)   by writing I, II etc. or any other recognized symbols on the dotted lines below;

OR   (b)   by writing notes on the staves.

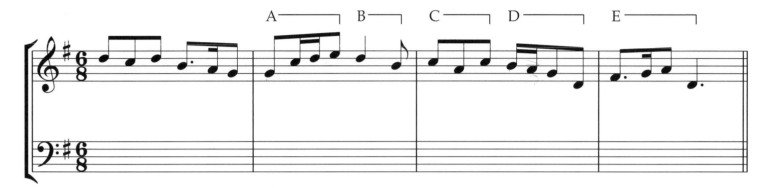

FIRST CADENCE:

Chord A   ....

Chord B   ....

SECOND CADENCE:

Chord C   ....

Chord D   ....

Chord E   ....